PAGLIACCI

Opera in Two Acts

Words and Music by

Ruggiero Leoncavallo

English Version by
JOSEPH MACHLIS

ED. 2560

G. SCHIRMER *New York/London*

Note

G. SCHIRMER, INC.

609 Fifth Avenue

New York 17, N. Y.

PAGLIACCI

Ruggiero Leoncavallo (1858-1919) was born in Naples, the son of a magistrate. He received his training at the conservatory of his native city. The struggling young composer gave piano and voice lessons to keep from starving, accompanied café-concerts, and in the latter capacity traveled widely. After many disappointments in his career as an operatic composer, he wrote *Pagliacci* (Clowns) for the publishing house of Sonzogno in Milan. The opera, produced when Leoncavallo was thirty-four years old, brought him international fame.

Pagliacci occupies the same position in Leoncavallo's life as its companion piece, *Cavalleria Rusticana*, does in Mascagni's. Each work represents a solitary success that its composer vainly tried to duplicate in his subsequent operas. Both works, too, mark the trend toward realism (*verismo*) that manifested itself in the Italian lyric theater at the end of the nineteenth century. Under the influence of *verismo*, composers began to favor subjects drawn from the life of the common people, presented in swift-moving dramas characterized by a passionate—at times even savage —intensity.

Pagliacci shows Leoncavallo's operatic gift at its most compelling. The work is enormously helped by the dramatic libretto which the composer himself wrote. The play-within-a-play, in which actors re-enact on the stage a situation that has impinged on their personal lives, is a theme that has attracted numerous dramatists, involving as it does the relationship between make-believe and reality. As a matter of fact Leoncavallo was sued for plagiarism by another author. He defended himself by explaining that he remembered a real case of a murder occurring in a traveling theatrical troupe under circumstances similar to those presented in his opera, his father having been the judge at the trial. The suit was withdrawn.

Pagliacci received its premiere at the Teatro dal Verme in Milan on May 21, 1892. The first American performance took place in New York on June 15, 1893. The work was presented at the Metropolitan Opera House on December 11 of that year, with Nellie Melba singing the role of Nedda, Fernando de Lucia as Canio and Mario Ancona as Tonio.

J.M.

THE STORY

The action takes place in a village in Calabria during the Feast of the Assumption. In the prologue, Tonio appears before the curtain to explain to the audience that the play they are about to see is no fantasy but is, as he says, "a picture of life," presenting the emotions and passions of real men and women.

ACT I. The curtain rises on a little square in a typical Italian village. To the right we see a modest traveling theater. The villagers, dressed in their holiday best, hail the arrival of a troupe of strolling players—especially Canio, "the prince of comedians." Canio, the head of the troupe, urges the crowd to attend the performance to be given that night. He goes off with some of the villagers for a glass of wine at the nearest tavern.

Tonio the hunchback, the clown of the company, remains behind to finish his chores. Finding Canio's wife, Nedda, alone, he takes the liberty of declaring his love for her. She scorns him. When he insists on a kiss, she grabs a whip and strikes him. Cringing with pain, Tonio swears that she will pay dearly for this.

No sooner has Tonio gone off than Silvio appears. He is the young villager with whom Nedda has been having a romance. He tries to persuade her to leave her husband and run away with him. Nedda at first refuses. Ultimately she gives in to Silvio's impassioned pleading. Tonio, on his way to the tavern, catches sight of the lovers and sees his opportunity for revenge: he runs off to fetch Canio. The enraged husband arrives just in time to hear Nedda promise that she will meet Silvio later that night. At Canio's approach Silvio escapes into the woods. Canio demands that Nedda reveal to him the name of her lover. She refuses. Canio, beside himself, is about to kill her when Peppe, another member of the troupe, stops him. Peppe reminds Canio that the villagers are assembling for the performance, and tells Nedda to get dressed for the play. There follows Canio's famous outcry of despair: he must go on the stage as Pagliaccio—the Clown—and make people laugh, even though his heart is breaking.

ACT II. The villagers gather for the play. There is great excitement as they pay admission and find seats. The play presented by Canio and his little troupe centers around the theme that has been a staple item of popular comedy for centuries: the trusting husband deceived by a faithless wife. Tonio plays the part of the stupid servant Taddeo, who declares his love for Columbine (Nedda), only to be scorned by her. Peppe plays the role of Columbine's lover, Harlequin. Their intimate little supper is interrupted by the unexpected arrival of the husband, Pagliaccio (Canio). Harlequin escapes through the window as Nedda promises to meet him later that night, using the same words as she did to Silvio that afternoon. As Canio proceeds to play his part, make-believe gradually retreats before the tragic reality of his situation. He insists that Nedda reveal the name of her lover. She laughs him off and tries to continue the comedy; the audience is amused. But Canio, carried away, reproaches her with her ingratitude and her betrayal. The spectators are deeply moved; some of them begin to wonder whether the actors are playing parts or are in earnest. Nedda reminds Canio that she has never been a coward and persists in her refusal to name the man she loves. Pushed beyond the breaking point, Canio seizes a knife from the table and stabs Nedda. With her last breath she cries out for Silvio, who has been watching the play. He runs to the stage to help her but is too late. Canio, now aware that Silvio was his wife's lover, stabs him to death. Amid the agitation of the horrified onlookers, Canio stands as in a trance and lets the knife fall from his hand, murmuring, "The comedy is ended!"

J.M.

CAST OF CHARACTERS

CANIO, head of a troupe of strolling players (Pagliaccio in the play) . . . Tenor

NEDDA, his wife (Columbine in the play) . . . . Soprano

TONIO, a member of the troupe (Taddeo in the play) . . . . Baritone

PEPPE, a member of the troupe (Harlequin in the play) . . . . Tenor

SILVIO, a villager . . . . Baritone

Peasants and Villagers

PLACE: A village in Calabria, Italy

TIME: In the 1860's

INDEX

Pagliacci
Drama in Two Acts
Prologue

English Version by
JOSEPH MACHLIS

Words and Music
R. Leoncavallo

Copyright © 1963, by G. Schirmer, Inc.

Printed in U.S.A.

8

Andantino sostenuto
(*Recitando*, or in unison with the Violoncello)

Poi - chè in iscena ancor le antiche ma - schere met-te l'au-

Once a - gain the au - thor tried to fol - low the an - cient

Andantino sostenuto (♩ = 52)

Pic.
Fl.

Harp
Str.

(dopo l'orchestra)

a tempo

to - re; in parte ei vuol ri - pren-de-re___ le vecchie u-

po - ets. He wish-es to re - vive for you___ the clas - sic

a tempo

col canto

Str.
Horns

rit.

san - ze, e a vo - i di nuo-vo in - via - mi.

dra - ma, and asks me to come be - fore you.

col canto

45607

Un po' meno presto che nell' Introd^{ne}(♩.= 80)

Ma non per dir - - vi co - me pria:
Ma - ny a time peo - ple have said:

»Le la - cri - me che noi ver - siam son fal - se!
"The tears that they shed are not real . . . they're act - ing.

De - gli spa - si - mi e de' no - stri mar - tir
And their suf - fer - ing need not move o - ur hearts.

non al - lar - ma - te - vi!«
it but make-be - lieve!"

animando a poco a poco

Dun-que, ve - dre - te_a - mar sì co - me
There-fore he writes of love the vio - lent

s'a - ma - no gli_esseri_u - ma - ni; ve - dre-te de l'o - dio i
pas - sions of hu - man be - ings; he tells you of hate and its

tri - sti frut-ti. Del do - lor gli spa - si - mi, ur - li di rab - bia,u -
tra - gic end-ing. You will see love's a - go-ny, fear-ful des-pair and

dre - te, e ri - sa ci - ni - che!
vio - lence, and cru - el mock - e - ry!

poi - chè siam uo - mi - ni di car - ne e
We too are men like you, we share hu - man

d'os - - sa, e che di que -
weak - - ness. Just like you, be -

st'or - fa - no mon - do al pa - ri di voi spi - ria - mo
wil - dered and help - less, we go through this lone - ly world in

l'ae - re! Il con - cet - to vi dis - si... Or a - scol -
dark - ness. This the au - thor in - ten - ded. Now see how

ta - te co - m'e - glie svol - to. An - diam. In - co - min - cia - - -
he un - fol - ded his sto - ry. Let's go! The cur - tain is ris - - -

Tempo I. Vivace

te!
ing!

Act I

Scene I

Scene. The entrance of a village – where two roads meet. On right a travelling theatre. As the curtain rises, sound of a trumpet out of tune and a drum are heard. Laughing, shouting, whistling, voices approaching. Enter villagers in holiday attire. Tonio looks up road on left; then, annoyed by the crowd which stares at him, lies down in front of the theatre. Time 3 o'clock. Bright sunlight.

tro!_____   Vi - va   Pa-gliac-cio,
way!_____   Hail to   Pa-gliac-cio!

tro!_____   Vi - va   Pa-gliac-cio,
way!_____   Hail to   Pa-gliac-cio!

tro!_____   Vi - va   Pa-gliac-cio,
way!_____   Hail to   Pa-gliac-cio!

to!_____   Vi - va Pa-gliac-cio,   vi - va Pa-gliac-cio,
ven!_____   Welcome, Pa-gliac-cio!   Welcome, Pa-gliac-cio!

tro!_____   Vi - va Pa-gliac-cio,   vi - va Pa-gliac-cio,
way!_____   Welcome, Pa-gliac-cio!   Welcome, Pa-gliac-cio!

to!_____   Vi - va Pa-gliac-cio,   vi - va Pa-gliac-cio,
ven!_____   Welcome, Pa-gliac-cio!   Hail to   Pa-gliac-cio!

to!_____   Vi - va Pa-gliac-cio,   vi - va Pa-gliac-cio,
ven!_____   Welcome, Pa-gliac-cio!   Hail to   Pa-gliac-cio!

sei dei pa - gliac - ci!   Ev - vi - va!
of all Co - me - dians!   Be wel-come!

sei dei pa - gliac - ci!   E - vi - va!
of all Co - me - dians!   Be wel-come!

sei dei pa - gliac - ci!   Ev - vi - va!   Ev - vi - va!
of all Co - me - dians!   Be wel come!   Be wel-come!

sei dei pa - gliac - ci!   Ev - vi - va!   Ev - vi - va!
of all Co - me - dians!   Be wel come!   Be wel-come!

Ev - vi - va!   Ev-vi-va! il prin - ci - pe
Be wel-come!   We glad-ly hail the Prince

Ev - vi - va!   Ev-vi-va! il prin - ci - pe
Be wel-come!   We glad-ly hail the Prince

Ev - vi - va!   Ev - vi - va!   Ev-vi-va! il prin - ci - pe
Be wel-come!   Be wel-come!   We glad-ly hail the Prince

Ev - vi - va!   Ev - vi - va!   Ev-vi-va! il prin - ci - pe
Be wel-come!   Be wel-come!   We glad-ly hail the Prince

poco rit.

vi - va! | Tu scac-ci i | guai co'l lie-to u - mor! | O -
wel-come! | Your laugh-ter | drives a - way our cares! | So

vi - va! | Tu scac-ci i | guai co'l lie-to u - mor! | O -
wel-come! | Your laugh-ter | drives a - way our cares! | So

vi - va! | Tu scac-ci i | guai co'l lie-to u - mor! |
wel-come! | Your laugh-ter | drives a - way our cares! |

vi - va! | Tu scac-ci i | guai co'l lie-to u - mor! |
wel-come! | Your laugh-ter | drives a - way our cares! |

Orchestra

poco rit.

a tempo un poco più sostenuto

gnun, | o - gnun | ap - plau-de a' mot-ti, ai laz - zi... Ed
hail | and cheer | the Prince of all Co - me - dians! But

gnun, | o - gnun | ap - plau-de a' mot-ti, ai laz - zi... Ed
hail | and cheer | the Prince of all Co - me - dians! But

O - gnun, | o - gnun ap - plau-de a' mot-ti, ai laz - zi...
So hail | and cheer the Prince of all Co - me - dians!

O - gnun, | o - gnun ap - plau-de a' mot-ti, ai laz - zi...
So hail | and cheer the Prince of all Co - me - dians!

a tempo un poco più sostenuto

f

ei,   ed ei   se - rio sa - lu - ta,e   pas - sa...
see!   He bows,   and pas - ses us po - lite - ly!

Sopr. I

ei,   ed ei   se - rio sa - lu - ta,e   pas - sa...
see!   He bows,   and pas - ses us po - lite - ly!

Sopr. II

ei,   ed ei   se - rio sa - lu - ta,e   pas - sa...
see!   He bows,   and pas - ses us po - lite - ly!

Ten. I

Ed ei,   ei se - rio   sa - lu - ta,e   pas - sa...
But see!   He bows, he   bows   so po - lite - ly!

Ten. II

Ed ei,   ei se - rio   sa - lu - ta,e   pas - sa...
But see!   He bows, he   bows   so po - lite - ly!

Bass I

Ed ei,   ei se - rio   sa - lu - ta,e   pas - sa...
But see!   He bows, he   bows   so po - lite - ly!

Bass II

Ed ei,   ei se - rio   sa - lu - ta,e   pas - sa...
But see!   He bows, he   bows   so po - lite - ly!

qua - le ma - tas - sa d'in - tri-ghi_or-di - rà._____
ras - cal whose ly - ing Will thick-en the plot._____

rit.

Ve - ni - - te,o - no - ra - te
So come_____ one and all,_____ my

sf con eleganza

ci si - gno - - rie si - gno - - re.   A
friends, We hope_____ for your pre - - sence!   To -

cedendo   *rall.*
                   con grazia

più lento

ven - ti - trè o - - re!   A ven - ti - trè o - -
night at e - le - - ven!   To - night at e - le -

più lento   col canto

(taking Nedda in his arms and lifting her down)

Via di lì!
Get a - way!

Sopr.
(laughing)
Ah! ah! ah! ah!
Ha! ha! ha! ha!

Ten.
(laughing)
Ah! ah! ah!
Ha! ha! ha!

Bass
(laughing)
Ah! ah! ah!
Ha! ha! ha!

Boys (Peppe drags off the cart) (making fun of him)

Con sa - lu - te!
What a beau - ty!

Sopr. I Soli (to Tonio)

Pren - di que - sto, bel ga - lan - te!
Take a hint, you gal - lant lo - ver!

Tonio threatens the boys, who run up the stage to back, and disappears grumbling behind the travelling theatre)

Tonio (aside, as he goes)

(Tonio enters the theatre)

La pa‿ghe‿ra‿ ‿ ‿ i! bri‿gan‿te!
He will re‿ gret this, I swear it!

(Four or five villagers approach Canio)

A Villager (to Canio)

Di', con noi vuoi be‿ve‿re un buon bic
Say, if you can spare the time, why don't you

chie‿ re sul‿ la cro‿ce‿vi‿a? Di', vuoi tu?
have a drink with us at the ta‿vern? Come with us!

Cantabile (♩=50)
Adagio molto *con grande espressione*

Un tal gio-co, cre-de-te-mi,— è meglio non gio-car-lo con me, miei
Such a joke,— I'd have you know,— would not be ve-ry plea-sant, My friends, be-

p legatissimo

ca-ri; e a To-nio... e un po-co a tut-tior par-lo! Il te-
lieve me. I say this to all who'd like to try it. For the

cantato

a -tro e la vi- -ta non son la stessa co-sa;
stage is il-lu- -sion, but life's an-o-ther mat-ter...

marcato

e legato il basso

no... non son la stes-sa co- -sa!!...
Yes, in-deed... an-o- -ther mat- -ter!...

rit.

(Canio approaches Nedda and kisses her forehead)

Scene and Chorus of the Bells

Meno ($\bullet$ = 160)

(Oboe within)

Boys

I zam - po - gna - ri!
Here come the bag-pipes!

(rushing to the left and looking off)

Sopr.

Soli I

I zam - po - gna - ri!
Here come the bag-pipes!

Villagers

Bass

Soli I

Ver - so la chie - sa
And now to church, it's

Cantabile legato con

Es - si ac - com-
See how the

van - noi com - pa - ri.
time for the ser - vice.

dolcezza e senza rall.

pa - gna - no la co - mi - ti - va che a cop - pie al ve - spe - ro
vil - la - gers hur - ry to pray - er. Dressed in their ho - li - day

Oboe within

Violin

p con eleganza

Bell

Bell

sen va giu - li - va.
best and so jol - ly.

Le cam - pa - ne...
Hear the church- -bells!

Bell

diam! / go! An - diam, an - diam, an - diam! / It's time to go to church!

diam! / go! An - diam, an - diam, an - diam! / It's time to go to church!

diam! / go! An - diam, an - diam, an - diam! / It's time to go to church!

l. h.   *l. h.*

Bell   Bell   Bell

(both groups join and form in couples)

Bell   Bell   Bell   Bell   Bell   Bell

Bell   Bell   Bell   Bell   Bell   Bell

ten-ti com-par! Ah!___ Ah!____ Le mamme cia-doc-chia-no at-
young men be-ware! Ah!____ Ah!____ Our mo-thers are watch-ing.__ Let __

di-tia-ma-dor! Ah!___ Ah!____ I vec-chi sor-ve-glia-no gli ar-
youth-ful de-light! Ah!____ Ah!____ The old_folks sus-pect the worst_ of_

dia di lu-ce e d'a-mor! Don Din Don Din Don Din
love, so ra-di-ant and bright!_ Dong, ding dong, ding dong, ding

cresc. *poco a poco*

poco rit.

ten-ti com-par! Din Don Din Don Din Don Din Don Din Don
young_men_be - ware! Ding dong, ding dong, ding dong, ding dong, ding dong,

di-tia-ma-dor! Din Don Din Don Din Don Din Don Din Don
youth-ful_de - light! Ding dong, ding dong, ding dong, ding dong, ding dong.

poco rit.

Don Din Don Din Don Din Don Din Don Din Don Din Don
dong, ding dong, ding dong, ding dong, ding dong, ding dong, ding dong.

poco rit.

cresc.

ff *rit. col canto*

64

45607

(The couples go off by road at back)

Scene II (Nedda alone, then Tonio)

Andante con moto ($\quad$ = 88)

Qual fiam - ma a-vea nel guar-do!
His eyes were bright with an - ger!

Gli oc-chi ab-bas - sa - i per te ma ch'ei leg - ges - se il
I looked a - way, for my heart was full of fear that he

mi - o pen-sier se - gre - to! Oh! s'ei mi sor-pren-
might dis - co - ver my se - - cret. Oh, if e - ver he should

des - se... bru - ta - le co - me e - gli è!
catch me, How cru - el he would be!

Ma ba - sti, or - vi - a. Son que-sti so - gni pa - u - ro - si e fo - le!
How fool-ish these fan - cies! I must not let such fear-ful dreams op-press me!

Ballatella

Vivace (♩.= 66)
in Uno come uno scherzo

pp
bisbigliando

* If the singer wishes to omit the trills, the orchestra goes to the bar marked ⅌, skipping one measure

tut - - to sfi - dar; _____ la piog - gia i
fi - - - ant and free. _____ No rain or

lam - pi, nul - la mai li ar - re - -
light - - ning can re - strain their cou - -

sta, e van - no e van - - no su - gli a
rage . . . They has - - ten on - - ward o - ver

bis - si e i mar. _____
land and sea. _____

con anima e passione allarg. la frase e ben cantato

ben cantato con la voce

Van - -no lag - giù _____ ver-
High up a - bove, _____ toward

so un pa - e - se stra - -no che
some mys - te - rious re - -gion, Dream - - -

so - gnan for - -se e che cer - -ca no in
ing of is - -lands that they may seek in

van. _____ Ma i bo - ë - mi del ciel _____
vain: _____ Min - strels of the sky, _____

Scena and Duet

Andante mosso — Nedda (sharply) — *sgarbatamente*

Sei là? cre - dea che te ne fos-si an -
It's you? I thought you had gone to the

sf

da - to!
ta - vern!

Andantino cantabile

Tonio — *con dolcezza*

È col - pa del tuo can - to.
I stayed, charmed by your sing - ing!

Andantino cantabile (♪ = 126)

rit.

Af - fa - sci - na - to io mi be - a - va!
Your voice so love-ly, I was en - rap - - tured!

rall.

col canto

rit.

Sostenuto

Nedda (laughing mockingly)

N. Ah! ah! Quan-ta po - e - si - a!... Va,
Ha, ha! Just — like a po - et ! Go!

T. Non ri - der, Ned-da!
Ned-da, don't mock me !

Sostenuto (♩ = 72)

affrett.

N. va al-l'o - ste - ri - a!
Go to your tav - ern!

T. So
I

Cantabile sostenuto (♩ = 116)

T. ben che dif - for - me, con-tor - to son i - o; che de-sto sol-tan - to lo
know I am ug - ly, my bo - dy re-pul-sive; I know that con-tempt — is my

scher - no e l'or - ror. ____ Ep - -pu - re ha'l pen - sie - ro un
lot in this world. ____ Yet I, too, can dream, I feel a

so - gno, un de - sì - o, e un pal - pi - to il cor! ____ Al -
pas - sion - ate long - ing, de - sire fills my heart! ____ And

rit.

rit. col canto

Poco più mosso

lor che sde - gno - - sa mi pas - si d'ac - can - - to, non
when you pass by me, so proud and dis - dain - - ful, Can

sai tu che pian - - to mi spre - me il do - lor! _____ Per -
you e - ver fa - - thom my sor - row, my pain? _____ But

rit. molto

qui che vo-glio dir - te - lo,
now I have to speak to you!

e tu m'a - scol - te - ra - - -
And I in - sist you 'hear

i, che t'a - - - mo e ti de -
me: I love you! You are my

Duet Scene III. Silvio and Nedda, then Tonio.

Un poco più mosso

ver - na ho scor-to!... Ma pru - den - te per la
wine in the ta - vern. Do not wor - ry. When I

Nedda

E an - co - raun po - co
A mo - ment soon - er,

mac - chiaa me no - ta qui ne ven - ni.
came, I made cer - tain no one saw me.

in To - nio t'im - bat - te-vi! Il gob-boè da te-
you would've been seen by To-nio. He could be ve-ry

(laughing)

Oh! To-nioil gob-bo!
Oh! To-nio the hunch-back!

con fuoco

S. E quan-do tu di qui___ sa-rai par-ti-ta, che ad-
What shall I do when you___ are gone, be-lov-ed? Oh,

incalz.

a tempo

poco rit. *affrett.* *poco ten.*

S. di - ver - rà___ di me... del - la mi - a vi -
how can I bear___ my grief when my dar-ling has left

col canto *col canto* *ten.*

Nedda (moved) *p mormorando*

N. Sil - - vio!
Sil - - vio!

con anima, a voce spiegata

S. ta?! Ned - da, Ned-da, ri -
me? Ned - da, why don't you

rit. *mf*

per - - der la vi - ta mia?_____
ruin my life_____ for e - - ver?

Ta - - ci Sil - vio, non più... È de - li - -
Dear - - est Sil - vio, no more of this mad - -

ro, è fol - lì - - a!
ness, I beg you!

too long, omit from ⊕ to 𝄋, page 107.

cominciando ad animare

tà?!_____ Se tu scor-da - sti
light?_____ Can you for-get those

col canto

l'o - re fu-ga - ci, io non lo pos - - so, e
hours__ to-ge - ther? Can you for-get all the

cresc. *con entusiasmo*

vo - glio an-cor, que' spa-smi ar-den - - ti,
joy__ we shared? Sweet-est re - mem - - brance,

rit. *molto* *riten.*

que' cal - di ba - ci, che tan - ta feb - - bre m'han mes-so in
e - choes of pass-ion de - li - ri - ous rap - - ture live in my

col canto

con fuoco *rit.*

Più mosso

perdutamente con passione

(Nedda overcome and yielding)

Nedda

cor!____ Nul - la scor - dai... ____ scon-vol - ta_e tur -
heart!____ Can I for - get? ____ Oh no, my be -

ba - ta ____ m'ha que - sto_a -
lov - ed! ____ When I re -

mor che ne'l guar - - do ti ____ sfa
mem - ber your love, ____ my heart is en

vil - la! ____ Vi - ver
chan - ted. ____ Could I

con tutta l'anima

vo - glio a te av - vin - - - ta, af - fa - sci -
hold you for - e - - - ver with my de -

na - - - ta, u - na vi - ta d'a -
vo - - - tion... If I on - ly could

mor cal - - ma e tran - quil - - -
share my life with you a -

la! A te mi
lone! Ah, I sur -

f delirante incalz. sempre

col canto

Scena and Finale I

(Tonio and Canio appear from the crossroad)

(half over the wall and holding to it)

Silvio

S.

Ad al - ta not - te lag - giù mi ter -
To - night at mid - night I'll wait for you

(leaping over)

S.

rò. Cau - ta di - scen - di e mi ri - tro - ve -
here. Dear - est, be care - ful be sure that no - one

(disappearing)

Nedda (to Silvio)

S.

ra - i. A sta - not - te e per
sees you. Un - til mid - night... I'll be

Lo stesso tempo
(Nedda turns at the shout, and seeing Canio, calls toward the wall)

N.

sem - pre tua sa - rò. Fug - gi!
yours for - e - ver - more! Hur - ry!

Canio (from where he is standing overhears the words, and shouts) (shouting)

S.

Ah!
Ah!

Lo stesso tempo

rit.

anio rushes to the wall, Nedda bars his way. Short struggle; he pushes her aside and leaps over the wall)

Concitato (♩ = 120)

sa - vo!
pect - ed!

(interrupting her)

Ma di far as-sai me-glio non di-spe-ro!
In the fu-ture, Per-haps I will do bet-ter!

col canto

brez - zo!
vil - lain!

Oh non sai co - me lie - to ne
Ah, this de - lights me More than I can

largamente

marcato

f

Mosso (♩ = 120)
(Canio reënters from over the wall, out of breath and mopping his forehead)

son!
say!

concitato senza affrettare a movimento preciso

Canio (with suppressed anger)

De-ri-sio - ne e scher-no!
To be mocked and help-less!

Nul-la! Ei ben lo co
Va-nished! That shows you how

no - sce quel sen - tier.
well he knows the path.

Fa lo stes-so;
It does not mat-ter

poi-chè del dru-do il
be-cause you're going to

Nedda (turning)

no - me or mi di - rai.
tell me Your lov-er's name.

Chi?!
Who?

Canio (starting in frenzy)

Tu, pel padre e - ter - no!...
You, by God in hea-ven!

(furiously to Nedda)

Moderato (♩= 84)
declamato

(drawing dagger from his belt)

E se in que - sto mo - men - to   qui scanna - ta   non t'ho   già,
And there's on - ly one   rea - son   Why I've not yet   slit your   throat:

Più mosso   *incalzando*

gli è per - chè pria di lor - dar - la nel tuo fe - ti - do sangue, o sver - go -
I must know with whom you be - trayed me! Yes, with whom you be - trayed me, you shame - less

incalzando

Nedda

Va - no è l'in-
Threats do not

gna - ta, co - de - sta la - ma, io vo'il suo no - me!... Par - la!!
wo - man! You'll have to name him, you'll have to tell me! Tell me!

col canto   *seguendo la declamazione*

re - ci - ta. Chis-sà ch'e-gli non ven-ga a lo spet-ta - co-lo
pare the play. Who knows? May-be he'll come to - night to see the show ...

misterioso *calando*

e si tra-di - sca! Or via. Bi - so-gna
And we'll un-mask him! Now come..., you must pre -

sotto voce

Peppe

(Peppe comes from the theatre)

p

(Tonio goes toward the back)

An-diamo, via,
It's get-ting late.

fin - ge-re per ri - u - scir!___
tend a-while, and we'll suc - ceed! ___

legato il basso e p sempre

(makes as if to go off, then turns to Tonio)

ve - sti - te - vi pa - dro - ne.
Go dress your-self, it's time now.

E tu bat - ti la cas - sa, To -
And beat your drum till we're rea - dy, To -

(both go off behind the theatre)   **Canio**

nio!   Reci - tar! Men - tre pre - so dal de - li -
nio!   To per-form! When my head's whir-ling with an -

rio non so più quel che di - co e quel che fac - cio! Ep-pur è
guish, not know-ing what I'm say - ing or what I'm do - ing! And yet I'll

string. un poco (angrily)

C. d'uo - po... sfor - za - ti! Bah! sei tu for-se un uom?
have to force my - self! Bah, can't you be a man?

col canto

precipitato

(laughing bitterly)
Ah!Ah!Ah!Ah! Ah!

rit. (taking his head in his hands in despair)

C. Tu se' Pa - gliaccio!
You're a Co - me - dian!

pp
K. dr.

Arioso
Adagio (♩ = 46)
declamando con dolore

C. Ve - sti la giub - ba e la fac - cia in -fa - ri - na. La gen - te
On with your cos - tume, and your face bright-ly pain - ted. Your pub - lic

pa - ga e ri - der vuo - le qua.___ E se Ar-lec - chin t'in -
pays you, and they must be a - mused.___ Though Co - lum - bine and

vo - la Co - lom - bi - na, ri - di, Pa - gliac-cio... e o - gnun ap-plau-di -
Har - le - quin be - tray you, Laugh, clown, be mer-ry and they will all ap -

rà! Tra - mu - ta in laz - zi lo spa - smo ed il pian - to;
plaud! You must trans - form___ your des - pair in - to laugh - ter;

affrett.   *cresc.*   *rit.*

in u-na smor-fia il sin - ghiozzo e'l do - lor... Ah! ____

And make a jest of your sob-bing, of your pain... Ah! ____

col canto

cresc.   *poco rit.*

a piena voce, straziante

Ri - di, Pa - gliac - cio,   sul tuo a - mo - re in -

Laugh and a - muse them,   though your love has be -

f molto rit.

con grande espressione   (sobbing)

fran - to! Ri - di del duol che t'av-ve - le - na il

trayed you! Laugh, through the tor - ment that em - bit - ters your

cedendo

(moves slowly towards the theatre, weeping; reaching the curtain which opens on the

cor! ____

heart! ____

Lo stesso movimento
cantabile con molta espressione

mf sonoro
r.h.

stage, he pushes it roughly, as if not wishing to enter; then, seized by a new

cresc. sempre

fit of sobbing, he again buries his face in his

f *poco rit. con dolore* *p* (The curtain begins to fall slowly)

hands; takes three or four steps towards the curtain, from which he had

rianimando

recoiled in fury, and [on these chords] enters and disappears)

rit. ed accentato molto

marcato il canto r.h.

End of Act I

Intermezzo

Act II

Peppe <u>comes from behind</u>, blowing a trumpet; Tonio follows, beating a big drum, and goes to take up his position on left of theatre. Meantime people come from all directions to the play, and Peppe places benches for the women.

Scene I. Men, Women and Chorus

Chorus

Sop. I

(from behind the scene)

Ohè!
Oho!

Ten. I

Ohè!
Oho!

ad lib.

Fl.

The first Basses enter left and approach the women, Sop. I, followed by Ten. II, Sop. II, and Bass II.

T.

Si dà prin - ci - pio a-van-ti a - van-ti!
We are be - gin-ning! Hur-ry, hur-ry!

pa - ri, ci af - fret - tiam.
go or we'll be late!

pa - ri, ci af - fret - tiam.
go or we'll be late!

ta - col co - min - ciar.
go or we'll be late!

ta - col co - min - ciar.
go or we'll be late!

ta - col co - min - ciar.
go or we'll be late!

ta - col co - min - ciar.
go or we'll be late!

(Silvio comes from back and

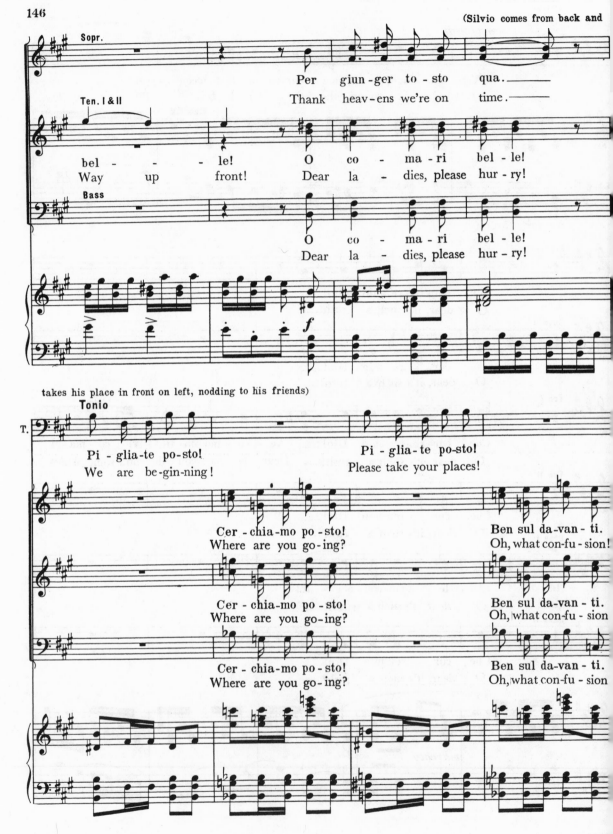

takes his place in front on left, nodding to his friends)

Cer - chiam di   met - ter - ci _____   ben   sul   da - van - ti,
Why don't we   look a - round _____   and   sit   to - ge - ther?

Cer - chiam di   met - ter - ci _____   ben   sul   da - van - ti,
Why don't we   look a - round _____   and   sit   to - ge - ther?

Cer - chiam di   met - ter - ci _____   ben   sul   da - van - ti,
Why don't we   look a - round _____   and   sit   to - ge - ther?

chè   lo spet - ta - co - lo _____   dee   co - min - cia - re.
Thank hea - vens we're on time,   the   play's be - gin - ning!

chè   lo spet - ta - co - lo _____   dee   co - min - cia - re.
Thank hea - vens we're on time,   the   play's be - gin - ning!

chè   lo spet - ta - co - lo _____   dee   co - min - cia - re.
Thank hea - vens we're on time,   the   play's be - gin - ning!

Sopr. I

da - te mai?__ per - chè tar - da - te? Siam tut-ti là!__
wait-ing for?__ We are quite read - y! Ev-'ry one's here!__

Sopr. II

da - te mai?__ per - chè tar - da - te? Siam tut-ti là!__
wait-ing for?__ We are quite read - y! Ev-'ry one's here!__

Ten. I

da - te mai?__ per - chè tar - da - te? Siam tut-ti là!__
wait-ing for?__ We are quite read - y! Ev-'ry one's here!__

Ten. II

da - te mai?__ per - chè tar - da - te? Siam tut-ti là!__
wait-ing for?__ We are quite read - y! Ev-'ry one's here!__

Bass I

da - te? per - chè tar - da - te? Siam tut-ti là!
wait - ing? We are quite read - y! Ev-'ry one's here!

Bass II

da - te? per - chè tar - da - te? Siam tut-ti là!
wait - ing? We are quite read - y! Ev-'ry one's here!

(Exit Tonio behind theatre, carrying away the big drum. Peppe goes to settle the women who are quarreling about their
seats)

Tonio

A - van-ti, a - van-ti, a-van-ti, a - van - ti!
This way, good peo - ple, hur-ry, hur - ry!

Sopr. I

Ma non pi - gia-te-vi,
Don't you go push-ing me!

Sopr. II

Ma non pi -
Don't you go

cresc. molto

Sopr. I
Su, su v'è po-sto ac-can - - - to!
Hur - ry, those seats are emp - - - ty!

Sopr. II
Pep - pe!
Pep - pe!
_ chia - mano a - iu - - - - - - - - to! V'è po-sto ac-
Go stop them, Pep - - - - - - - pe! Those seats are

Ten. I
chia - mano a - iu - - - - - - - - to! Veh!
Please go — stop them, Pep - - - - - - - pe! See!

Ten. II
Se - de - te, via, sen - za gri - dar.
Sit down, and don't make so much noise!

(Silvio passes on right, seeing Nedda going round with plate for the money, and approaches her)

Ma non pi - gia - te - vi,
Don't you go push - ing me!

can - to! V'è po-sto ac-can - to! Su; Pep - pe, a iu - ta - ci!
emp - ty! Let's sit to - ge - ther! Pep - pe, they're quar - rel - ing!

veh! Ma via se - de - te - vi!
See! Don't you go push - ing me!

(laughing)
Ah! Ah!
Ha! Ha!

p

(Nedda walks away, and goes on collecting money)

The Play

SCENE II. The curtain of the Theatre drawn aside. The scene, roughly painted, represents a little room with two side-doors, a practicable window at back, table and two common chairs on right. Nedda, dressed as Columbine.

Tempo di Minuetto ($\quarternote$ = 69)

(as the curtain opens, Columbine is seated near table; from time to time she

looks anxiously at the door on right)

(Columbine rises, goes to look out of window, and then returns to the front, walking about restlessly)

Columbine

Pa - gliac - cio mio ma - ri - - to
Pa - gliac - cio, my___ hus - band,

a tar - da not - te   sol ri - tor - ne - rà...
Won't be re - turn - ing   till ve - ry late to - night.___

SERENATA

Allegretto un poco moderato (♩=120)

(Columbine, hearing the sound of a guitar off the stage, rushes to window with a cry of joy, but does not open it)

Di___ te chia-man - do,e so - spi - ran - do a-spet - ta il po - ve - rin!___

See, I stand a - lone and sigh with long - ing as I wait for you!___

La___

Ah,___

___ tua fac - cet - ta mo - stra-mi, ch'io vo' ba - ciar sen - za tar -

Won't you show your lit - tle face that I may kiss— kiss you a -

poco rit.

col canto

a tempo

senza respirare

dar___ la tua boc - cuc - cia. A - mor mi

gain!___ O my be - lov - ed, how I a -

a tempo

di te chia - man - do, e so - spi - ran - do
Hear me, my dar - ling... I love you on - ly,

— è il po - ve - ro Ar - lec - chin!
— so faith - ful and so true!

Oboe

A te vi - cin
I wait for you!

a tempo

Flutes

è Ar - lec - chin!
Ah, so true!

sino alla fine

deciso

f

Scena Comica

Andantino sostenuto (♩=76)
con eleganza

Ta.

con eleganza

Ed an - zi, ec - - co - ci en -
Or bet - ter... I and the

tram - bi ai pie - di tuo - i!
chick - en be - fore you kneel - ing.

Poi - chè l'o - ra è suo - na - ta, o Co - lom -
For the hour is u - pon us when I'm re -

bi - na, di sve - lar - ti il mio cor!
veal - ing All the love in my heart!

du - ra, _____ du - ra ti
met you, _____ You've been so

mo - stri, du - ra, ad o - bli -
cru - el, cru - el. Yet I shall

sospeso

Harlequin

(taking Taddeo by the ear and kicking him)

Va a pigliar
Go take a

ar - ti nonri - e - sco! no! non riesco!
ne - ver, ne - ver for - get you! No, my dear - est!

Andantino sostenuto e grazioso (♩=72)

Duet. (Colum. and Harleq. gaze at each other with exaggerated fondness)

Ar-lec-chin! Colom - bi - na!
Har-le - quin! Co-lum - bine, dear!

Al-fin s'ar - ren - da ai no-stri prieghi a-
A-lone at last! Love has an-swered all our

mor!
prayers!

affrett.

Colum. *deciso*

Fac-ciam me -
And so to

col canto

(Columbine takes from table knives, forks and spoons for two, places the fowl on
table, while Harlequin takes up the bottle which he left on the ground.)

ren - - da.
sup - - per!

Guar - -
Please

r.h.

l.h.

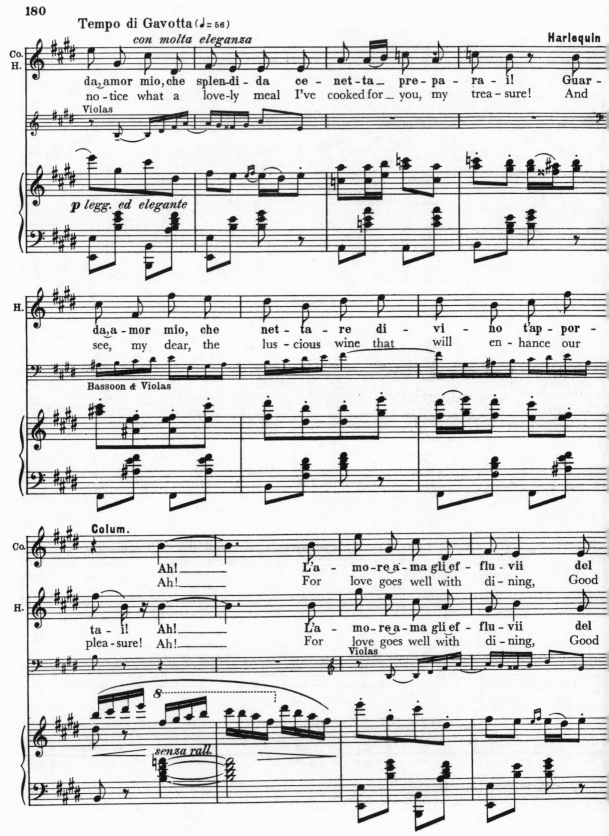

dal ― lo a Pa ― gliac-cio   pria che s'ad - dor - men-ti,   e
It's   for your hus-band.   This will make him sleep-y   While

poi fug-gia-mo insiem!   Sì,   por - gi!   At-
you and I es-cape.   Yes,   dear - est!   Be

Allegretto agitato (♩=169)   (enters with mock alarm)

ten ― ― ti!   Pa - gliac-cio...   è
care ― ― ful!   Pa - gliac-cio   is

là...   tut - to stra - vol - to...   ed ar - mi cer - ca!...   Ei sa
here!   He's ve - ry ang-ry . . . and wants to kill you!   Some-one

a - co?
drink - ing?

(restraining himself with difficulty)

Bri - a - co!
You think so?

(eyeing her with meaning)

si...
Yes!

da un' o - ra!!
I had to!

Nedda

Tor - na - sti pre - sto.
You're home so ear - ly.

(pointedly)

Ma in tem - po!
In time, though!

(going towards the door left)

che là si chiu - se per pa - u - ra!
But now you forced him in - to hid - ing.

Or - sù... par - la!
Come out! Tell him!

Tonio (from within, pretending to be afraid)
poco meno

Cre - de - te - la! Cre - de - te - la! Es - sa è
Be - lieve her, sir! She speaks the truth! She is

poco meno

marcato

(affectedly) *f* (sneering) *rall. molto* *ten.*

pu - - ra!! E ab - bor - re dal men - tir quel lab - bro
pure as snow! How could she tell a lie, when she's so

rall. col canto

188

45607

Andante mosso

Vo' il no - me de l'a - man - te tuo, del dru-do in-fa - me a cui ti

I de - mand to know your lo - ver's name... The vile be - tray - er who en -

de - sti in brac - cio, o tur - pe don - na!

joyed your kis - ses! Oh, you are shame-less!

Molto più mosso della Iª volta

Nedda (joking)

Pa - gliaccio!

Pa - gliaccio!

Pa - gliaccio!

Co - me - dian!

rit.

cresc. molto

Allegro moderato (♩= 144)

Canio

No! Pa - gliac - - cio non son;

No! Co - me - - dian I'm not!

sf

45607

C. se il vi - so è pal - li - do, è di ver
And if my face is white, it is for

C. go - gna, e sma - nia di ven - det -
hor - ror, for shame at my dis - hon -

C. ta! L'uom ri - pren - de i suoi
or! Now I see you be -

C. drit - ti, e'l cor che san - gui - na vuol san - gue
trayed me— my heart cries out for blood, for ven - geance

nel - la in su la vi - - - - a
found you so for - sak - - - - en,

qua - si mor - ta di fa - me,
Near - ly dy - ing of hun - ger.

e un no - me of-
I gave you a

fri - - a - ti,
home, a name,

ed un a - mor
A burn - ing love

ch' e - ra
that was

(falls overwhelmed on the chair, by table)

feb - - bre e fol - lì - a!
fol - - ly and mad - ness!

(laughter in the crowd, immediately checked by Canio's appearance) Canio *violento* *declam. a piac.*

no! / low!
Ah! _____ tu mi / Ah, _____ you de-

sfi-di! E an-cor non l'hai ca-pi-ta / fy me! You still don't un-der-stand me!

ch'io _____ non ti ce-do?... Il no-me, o la tua vi- / I _____ speak in ear-nest! You'll name him or I will kill

Nedda

(bursting out)
Ah! / No,

ta! il no-me! / you! Who was it?

(Peppe appears at back, held by Tonio)

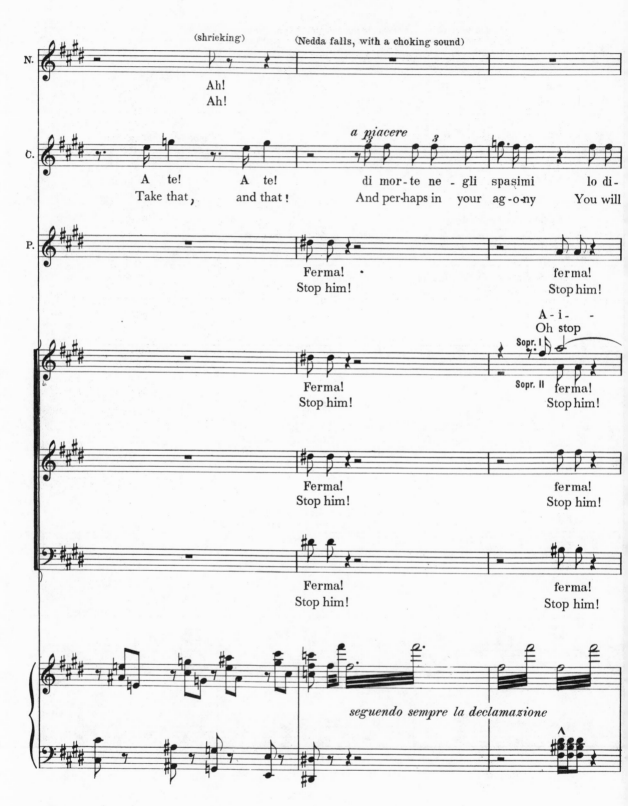

Maestoso larghissimo (♩=40)

(the curtain falls rapidly)

fff tutta la forza

più rit.

Vivo

End of the Opera